BRAIN GAMES™ kids

PUZZLE POWER!

Publications International, Ltd.

Puzzle Constructors: Cihan Altay, Ryan Browne, Keith Burns, Myles Callum, Clarity Media, Ltd., Jeff Cockrell, Garry Colby, Don Cook, Sean Dove, Harvey Estes, Marie Estes, Rick Ewigleben, The Grabarchuk Family, Peter Grosshauser, David Helton, Helene Hovanec, Robin Humer, Naomi Lipsky, Janet McDonnell, Fred Piscop, Stephen Ryder, Pete Sarjeant, Robbie Short, Jen Torche, Wayne Robert Williams, Alex Willmore

Illustrators: Chris Gattorna, Robin Humer, Jen Torche

Cover Puzzles: Peter Grosshauser

Brain Games is a trademark of Publications International, Ltd.

ISBN-13: 978-1-4508-4624-0
ISBN-10: 1-4508-4624-6

Manufactured in China.

8 7 6 5 4 3 2 1

CONTENTS

Get Ready for Fun and Games!

Look no further, kids! *Brain Games™ Kids: Puzzle Power!* is here, and it's jam-packed with brainteasers that will pump up your puzzle power and provide the fun. You'll find twisty mazes, illustrated puzzles, word riddles, and many more.

We've put our heads together to come up with a big-time collection of puzzles and loaded them into this handy, pocket-size book. Your favorite teasers are sorted into levels, so you can kick off with an easy one in the first level or fast-track straight to the toughest challenges in Level 3. Skip around and work a variety of puzzles—you'll have fun for days, and your mind will get the workout it needs!

Another thing to keep in mind is that every answer is included in the back of the book. You want to be sure to give each puzzle a try, but the solutions are there to get you back on track in case you get stuck.

Kids, now you're ready to get moving! So grab a pencil, and get your noggin cooking with *Brain Games™ Kids: Puzzle Power!*

Parent's note: The more than 115 kid-friendly brainteasers in *Brain Games™ Kids: Puzzle Power!* will hold your child's interest for hours while also giving their brains a boost and improving their language skills, analytic thinking, and logical reasoning.

Compact and portable, your youngsters can tote this mobile book everywhere they go—school, dance class, soccer practice, or a visit to the dentist's office. (It might even make the trip to a teeth scrubbing a little more fun!) So give them this book, and turn them loose on puzzling!

REV UP YOUR ENGINE
Rhyme Time

Circle the 5 words that rhyme with the word "gum"!

yum

drum

tree

thumb

gum

ant

crumb

hair

red

from

Answer on page 122.

Chain Words

Place 2 letters in the middle squares that will complete one word and start another. For example, ER would complete FLY - ER - ROR.

Flower Growth

Which of these flowers has the longest stem?

Answers on page 122.

Dot-to-Dot

Draw a line from consecutive numbers, starting at 1 and ending at 42, to reveal a cuddly toy.

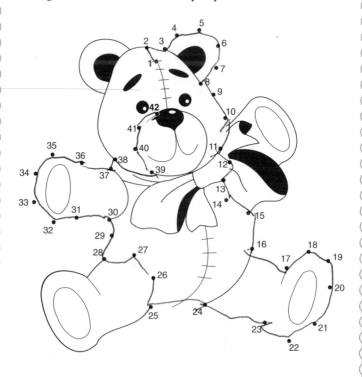

8   Answer on page 122.

Rock On!

Which guitarist is the mirror image of the one in the box?

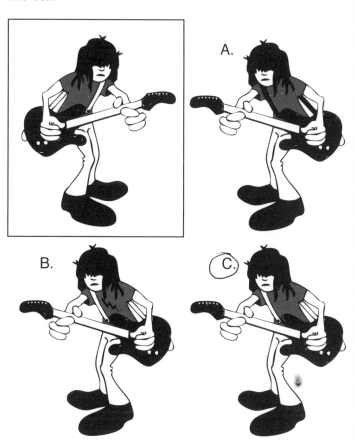

A.

B.

C.

Answer on page 122.

Alien Message

Use the code below to answer this riddle: What did the alien say to the gardener?

A   D   E   K   M   O

R   T   U   W   Y

"TAKE ME

TO YOUR

WEEDER."

Answer on page 122.

R Is for River

There are at least 10 things hidden in this picture beginning with the letter **R.** Can you find more than 10?

Answers on page 122.

Flippy Numbers

Below is an incorrect equation. Can you swap 2 of the number cards to get a correct equation?

Word Ladder

Can you change just one letter on each line to transform the top word to the bottom word? Don't change the order of the letters, and make sure you have a common English word at each step.

RING

Sing what you do in a choir

Sins bad deeds

Sons boys, to their parents

Tons lots and lots!

TOSS

Pic-doku

The grid below is divided into 4 sections. Your job is to have each of the 4 items appear once in each section and in each row and column. Fill each square with the item's image or the letter that represents it. No item can repeat in any section, row, or column.

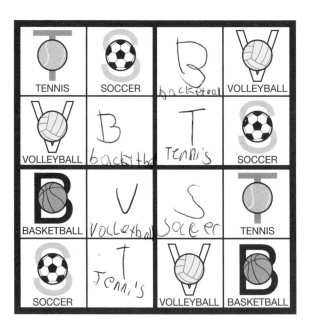

Answer on page 123.

One Small Step

Find all of these items below hidden in this stellar scene.

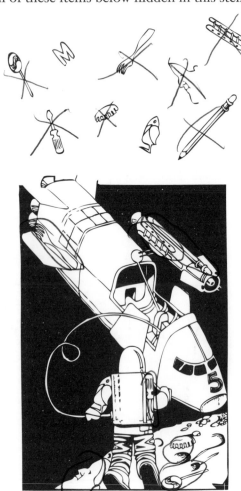

Answers on page 123.

Picture-by-Number

Shade in the numbers that are divisible by 2. Once complete, you will reveal a simple image.

84	98	73	47	57	3	18	20
8	10	3	37	69	29	56	76
15	65	7	93	23	63	47	47
61	65	35	56	92	11	35	47
33	27	97	68	28	21	3	85
83	87	99	23	39	1	55	67
90	95	91	91	27	37	11	52
64	100	34	10	6	28	76	28

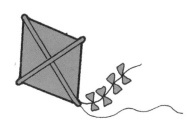

Answer on page 123.

Big Cheese

You'll need a sharp eye to find all 10 differences in these pictures!

17   Answers on page 123.

Tangle

Several shovels have been laid on the table, one by one.
Which one is on the bottom of the pile?

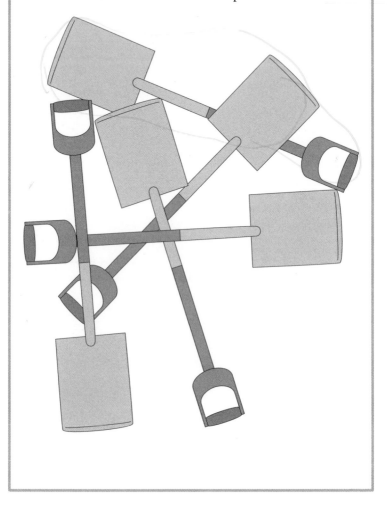

Answer on page 123.

Fairy Find

Looks like you've stumbled upon a group of funny fairies! Each row of fairies (horizontal and vertical) has one thing in common. Find each to solve the puzzle.

Answers on page 124.

Black Diamonds

Place the numbers 1 through 4 in the cells of each of the squares below. There's a catch though: Overlapping cells must add up to the number given in the black diamond.

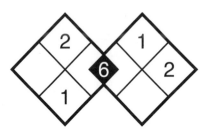

Chain Words

Place 2 letters in the middle squares that will complete one word and start another. For example, ER would complete FLY - ER - ROR.

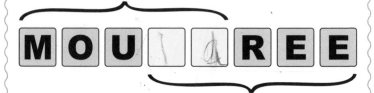

M O U ☐ ☐ **R E E**

Answers on page 124.

Family Ties

Divide the grid into 4 sections with each section containing 4 squares. Every section must contain one of each of the family members—mother, father, brother, and sister.

Hint: Look for places where the same family member is bunched together, and start there.

Answer on page 124.

Dot-to-Dot

Draw a line from consecutive numbers, starting at 1 and ending at 40, to reveal a zooming sailboat.

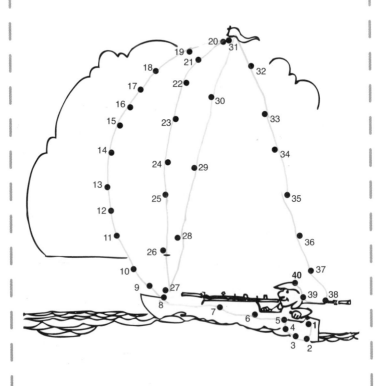

22   Answer on page 124.

A Bug's Life

Find the 4 creepy crawlers expertly hidden in this flowering scene.

23

Answer on page 124.

Dino Crusade

Help the lost dinosaur find his way home through this rocky maze.

24 Answer on page 125.

Rhyme Time

Each object on the left rhymes with one object on the right. When you find the rhyming pair, draw a line to connect them!

Answers on page 125.

Anagrammar

There are 2 words on this torn parchment that are anagrams (rearrangements of the same letters) of each other. Trace the lines to the connecting circle, and write in the identical letter to discover the second word.

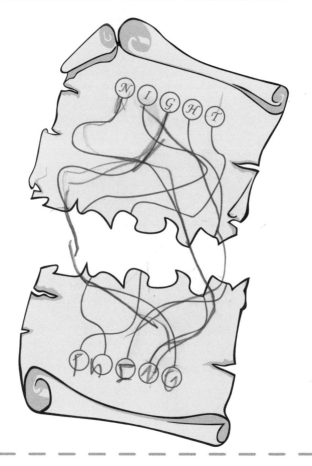

Answer on page 125.

Ice Capades

There's something slippery happening between these 2 illustrations! Can you find the 6 changes?

Answers on page 125.

Picture Day

Oh no, it rained! Help me get to school for picture day without getting my new shoes all muddy!

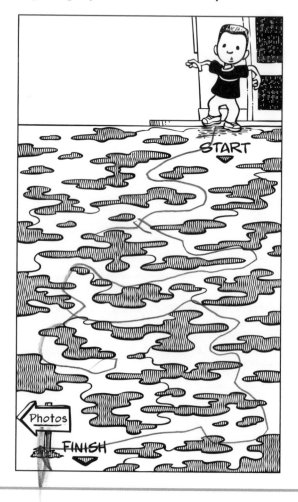

Answer on page 125.

Word Ladder

Can you change just one letter on each line to transform the top word to the bottom word? Don't change the order of the letters, and make sure you have a common English word at each step.

DOG

PET

Flower Growth

Which of these flowers has the longest stem?

A Bright Idea

Which bulb is the mirror image of the one in the box?

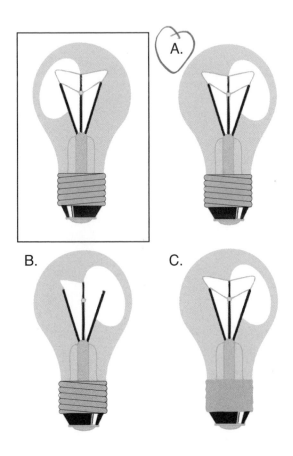

A.

B.

C.

Answer on page 126.

Mutation

Look at the 2 words on each line. Someone has not only scrambled the words from the left side to the right, but a letter has been removed as well! Figure out what that letter is, and write it in the blank. When you're done, read the letters going down to answer this riddle: Where does Lassie go on vacation?

CREAK _C_ RAKE

OCEAN _O_ CANE

DRAWL _L_ WARD

LOAFS _L_ SOFA

OLIVE _I_ LOVE

CREASE _E_ SCARE

SNIFF _F_ FINS

SMOOTH _O_ MOTHS

EARNS _R_ SANE

LISTEN _N_ TILES

UNITS _I_ STUN

SALAD _A_ LADS

Nine Fish Blots

Two of the blots below are identical in shape and color.
Can you find them?

32   Answer on page 126.

Rhyme Time

• •

Each clue leads to a 2-word answer that rhymes, such as BIG PIG or STABLE TABLE. The numbers in parentheses after the clue give the number of letters in each word. For example, "cookware taken from the oven (3, 3)" would be "hot pot."

1. Appreciates bicycles (5, 5): _likes bikes_

2. Unusual grizzly (4, 4): _____

3. Make a birthday dessert (4, 4): _Bake cake_

4. Out-of-control youth (4, 5): _____

5. Blinding sunshine (6, 5): _____

Chain Words

• •

Place 2 letters in the middle squares that will complete one word and start another. For example, ER would complete FLY - ER - ROR.

| G | H | O | | | A | R | T |

Answers on page 126.

School Daze

Looks like Sammy had a pretty big day! Arrange the pictures in the order in which they happened. Start at 1 and end at 4.

34

Answer on page 126.

Jumbled Up

Place each letter into the empty boxes below to create a common word. Letters are in the correct order, but they are not in the upright position.

So You Want to Be a Star!

Why is this guy smiling? Because he's a star! You'll be a star too once you complete this maze!

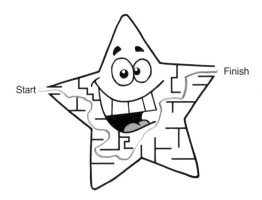

Start

Finish

Answers on page 126.

The Solar System

ACROSS

1. Barking sound
4. Admiration
7. Ms. Lane, who loved Superman
9. The red planet
11. Dwarf planet
12. Pull apart
13. Go bad
14. "_____, humbug!"
16. Lock opener
17. Boy's name (hidden in "shallow end")
19. Say words you shouldn't say
21. Planet beneath your feet
23. Take it easy
24. That girl's
28. Scrap of cloth
30. Busy _____ bee: 2 wds.
32. "Winnie-the-Pooh" character
33. Book of maps
35. 2nd planet from the sun
37. It orbits 21-Across
38. Just like you see it: 2 wds.
39. Chili holder
40. "Get it?"

DOWN

1. Let
2. Way of a mail carrier, for example
3. In shape
4. Electric guitars play through it
5. Goes on foot
6. One of the Great Lakes
8. Cry noisily
10. Pigpen
11. NFL player, for example
12. Close
15. Land divisions
18. Boy's name (hidden in "tone-deaf")
20. "Stop talking!"
22. "How awful!"
23. House made of ice
25. Bert's buddy
26. Cause to wake
27. Distress signal
28. Slam into
29. At the highest point of
31. Girl's name (hidden in "Havana")
34. Insect in a colony
36. Letter after ar

Answers on page 127.

Zoom

Identify the locations of the close-up pictures found below.

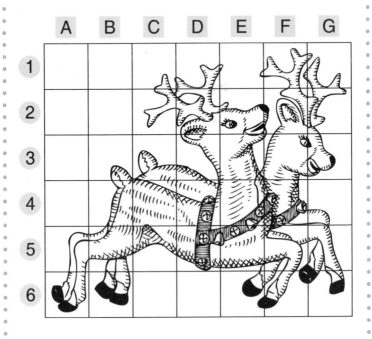

Answers on page 127.

Up in the Air

Only one of these kites has a string that doesn't have a gap. Which one? Follow the strings to find out!

 Answer on page 127.

Ahoy, Matey!

There are 16 things hidden in this picture that begin with the letter **P.** Can you find them all?

Answers on page 127.

Nine Pawprints Blots

Two of the blots below are identical in shape and color.
Can you find them?

Answer on page 127.

At the Petting Zoo

Every animal listed is contained within the group
of letters on the next page. Animals can be found in
a straight line diagonally. They may be read either
forward or backward. Leftover letters spell a "squeaky"
riddle.

CAMELS

CHICKENS

DONKEYS

DUCKS

GOATS

GUINEA PIGS

LLAMAS

PONIES

RABBITS

SHEEP

TORTOISES

TURKEYS

42

```
W H A D S T H A S S S
I X E K O S G N Y G E
S T C S H N E O U B U
S U O E A K K I A S T
D Y E R C M N E E T R
S P E I T E A I Y A S
C L H K A O N L B S A
N C E P R O I B L N O
T S I M P U I S E E T
H G R E A T T E E B L
S I N D S C M I C S E
```

Hidden message: _____

_____

43   Answers on page 128.

Family Ties

Divide the grid into 4 sections with each section containing 4 squares. Every section must contain one of each of the family members—mother, father, brother, and sister.

Hint: Look for places where the same family member is bunched together, and start there.

44   Answer on page 128.

PUT THE PEDAL TO THE METAL
Big Top Maze

Here's your ticket to the circus! Go in at the tent entrance and climb out at the top flag.

Finish

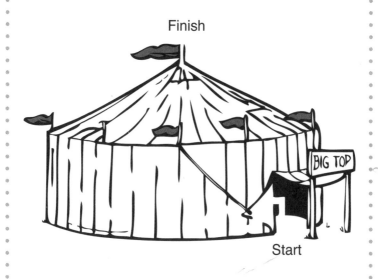

BIG TOP

Start

Answer on page 128.

Tangle

Several feathers have been laid on the table, one by one. Which one is on the bottom of the pile?

46

Answer on page 128.

Dot-to-Dot

Draw a line from consecutive numbers, starting at 1 and ending at 53, to reveal a musical instrument.

47 Answer on page 128.

Flippy Numbers

Below is an incorrect equation. Can you swap 2 of the number cards to get a correct equation?

Jumbled Up

Place each letter into the empty boxes below to create a common word. Letters are in the correct order, but they are not in the upright position.

Rhyme Time

Each object on the left rhymes with one object on the right. When you find the rhyming pair, draw a line to connect them!

Answers on page 129.

Haunted Scramble

Unscramble the letters to discover some spooky items!

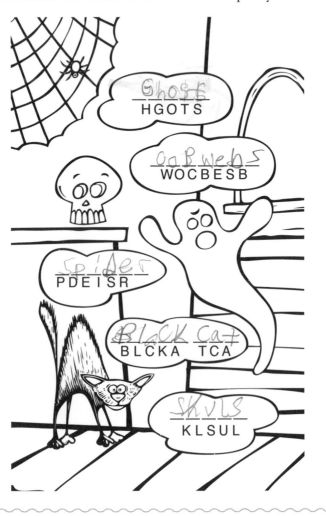

50   Answers on page 129.

Flower Growth

Which of these flowers has the longest stem?

51   Answer on page 129.

Swamp Things

Can you find the 14 creepy crawly bugs shown on the bottom in this swamp scene?

Answers on page 130.

Family Ties

Divide the grid into 9 sections with each section containing 4 squares. Every section must contain one of each of the family members—mother, father, brother, and sister.

Hint: Look for places where the same family member is bunched together, and start there.

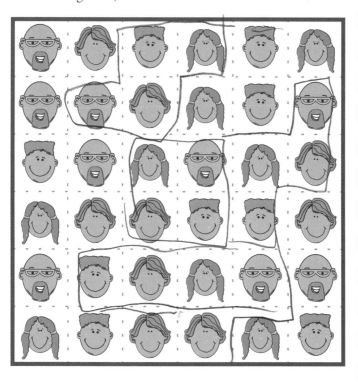

Answer on page 130.

Big Builder

Will you help me find the blocks I need? Follow the maze and find the red letters that complete the message!

54   Answers on page 130.

Nine Stars Blots

Two of the blots below are identical in shape and color.
Can you find them?

Answer on page 130.

Add It Up!

Solve the equations to discover which letter corresponds with which number. Use the answers to solve the riddle!

WHY DID THE MATH BOOK NEED GLASSES?

HE HAD PROBLEMS WITH

$\underset{13}{D}\underset{8}{I} - \underset{24}{V}\underset{8}{I}\underset{7}{S}\underset{8}{I}\underset{12}{O}\underset{15}{N}$

V = 12 + 12   D = 11 + 2

O = 5 + 7   N = 8 + 7

I = 6 + 2   S = 3 + 4

56   Answer on page 131.

Crosspic

Looks like someone put pictures in this puzzle where there are supposed to be words! See if you can fill in the grid by writing the word—one letter for each box—that names each of the pictures. Words run across and down.

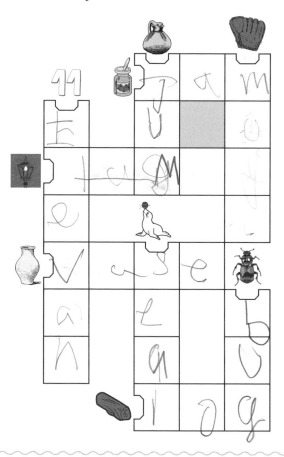

Answers on page 131.

Find the Differences

Can you spot all 10 wild changes in the wilderness scene?

59   Answers on page 131.

Road Trip!

This confused driver is having trouble finding the gas station—and he's running on empty! Follow the arrows to help him find the correct route.

Answer on page 131.

Take a Note

Which figure is the mirror image of the one in the box?

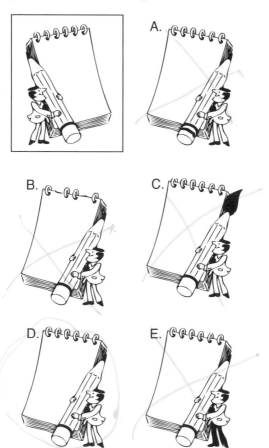

Answer on page 131.

Good Luck!

ACROSS

1. Opposite of good
4. Sketcher's tablet
7. Not very bright
10. It equals the number of cake candles
11. High card in a suit
12. Formal poem
13. Some say it's good luck: 2 wds.
16. Appliance for smoothing clothes
17. Boy's name (hidden in "pearly")
18. Negative vote
19. Painting and sculpture
20. Have a meal
21. Opposite of nah
23. Mas' opposite numbers
26. Wheel centers
27. "If it _____ broke, don't fix it!"
28. Some say it's good luck: 2 wds.
31. Shade tree
32. Cut (off)
33. "_____ had enough!"
34. Path or road

35. Distress signal letters
36. Allow

DOWN

1. Snickers _____ (candy treat)
2. One more time
3. Girl's name (rearrange "bread")
4. Achy feeling
5. Play a part in a play
6. Dry, sandy area
7. Ways into a house
8. Wildly popular star
9. Was introduced to
14. Baby in blue
15. Opposite of skinny
19. "Say _____" (doctor's order)
20. Artists' stands
21. Mmm, mmm, good!
22. Go out, like the tide
23. Little Jack Horner's dessert
24. A blacksmith hammers on it
25. Boy's name (rearrange "see TV")

26. Kind of hoop
27. Dangerous snakes
28. "Happy _____ Year!"
29. Pal of Pooh
30. It hangs from a basketball hoop

Hairdresser!

Uh-oh! Someone dropped 15 bobby pins into Gladys's hair! Can you find them all?

Answer on page 132.

Pic-doku

The grid below is divided into 4 sections. Your job is to have each of the 4 items appear once in each section and in each row and column. Fill each square with the item's image or the letter that represents it. No item can repeat in any section, row, or column.

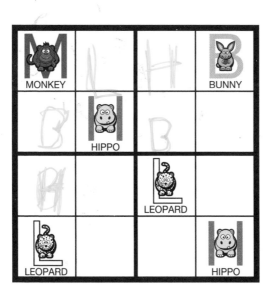

65   Answer on page 132.

After School

• •

There are 8 objects hidden in the picture below. Can you find them all?

BADGE

BOOK

BOWL

BUTTON

ENVELOPE

FEATHER

PENNANT

SOCK

66

Tangle

Several pairs of scissors have been laid on the table, one by one. Which one is on the bottom of the pile?

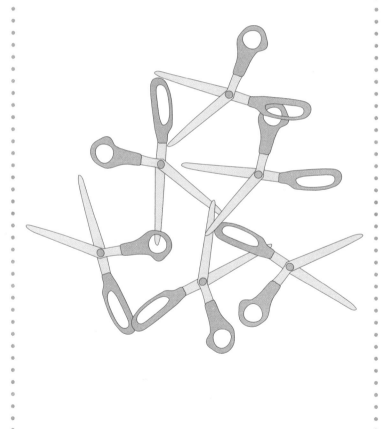

Answer on page 132.

Poolside Penguins

Something funny happened between these 2 illustrations—someone flipped some things around, and now there are 10 differences. Can you find them all?

Answers on page 133.

Flippy Numbers

Below is an incorrect equation. Can you swap 2 of the number cards to get a correct equation?

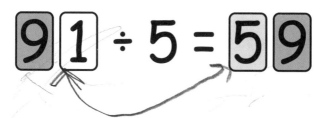

Flower Growth

Which of these flowers has the longest stem?

Answers on page 133.

Mouse Hunt!

Can you follow an "odd-even-odd-even" pattern and help the mouse get to the cheese? No diagonal connections, just sideways or up and down!

8	7	3	4	50	60	76	82
18	24	6	8	13	10	99	91
13	8	7	33	1	72	83	55
26	10	11	82	6	8	16	32
55	77	12	101	99	73	29	19
76	3	16	23	36	10	30	16
86	5	20	25	76	33	67	41
26	8	6	51	44	17	82	16
30	93	81	37	6	29	94	
42	20	90	89	2→			

Answer on page 133.

Distant Visitor

Which alien is the mirror image of the one seen in the box?

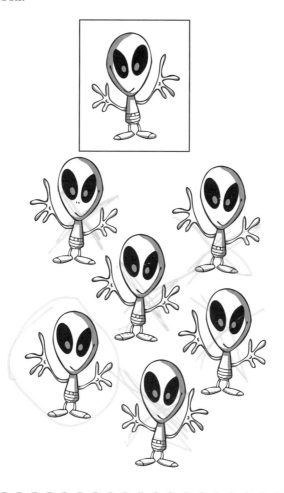

Answer on page 134.

Searching for Shrek!

Every "Shrek" character listed is contained within the group of letters on the next page. Characters can be found in a straight line horizontally, vertically, or diagonally. They may be read either forward or backward.

BIG BAD WOLF

BROGAN

COOKIE

CYCLOPS

DONKEY

DRAGON

DRONKEYS

FARKLE

FELICIA

FERGUS

FIONA

HAROLD

KING ARTIE

LILLIAN

LORD FARQUAAD

MERLIN

PINOCCHIO

PUSS IN BOOTS

RAPUNZEL

SHREK

WITCHES

```
A L O R D F A R Q U A A D
U M D N E I T R A G N I K
N I L R E M A I C I L E F
Z D G S S Y E K N O R D L
H U L P I N O C C H I O O
S T O O B N I S S U P N W
E P J L R Z A N B M A K D
H E T C E A F I A P A E A
C M Q Y M L H E L G N Y B
T W S C O O K I E L O V G
I I O N O G A R D G I R I
W H L E Z N U P A R F L B
F X O D N D P J G F I Z C
```

Answers on page 134.

L Is for Lunchtime

There are at least 10 things hidden in this picture beginning with the letter **L**. Can you find them all?

74

Answers on page 134.

Go Fish

Which line has hooked into the catch of the day?

Answer on page 134.

On Top of Spaghetti

Which lucky kid tangled the meatball?

Answer on page 135.

Family Ties

Divide the grid into 9 sections with each section containing 4 squares. Every section must contain one of each of the family members—mother, father, brother, and sister.

Hint: Look for places where the same family member is bunched together, and start there.

Answer on page 135.

Recess Scramble

• •

Unscramble the letters to create words of things you might find at recess!

ORGUDYNALP

PPROEMJU

EETTOEETRTTR

LDISE

GSINWS

TEKBLALBAS

Answers on page 135.

Nine Leaves Blots

Two of the blots below are identical in shape and color. Can you find them?

Answer on page 135.

Ski Fun

There are 10 things wrong in this snowy scene. Can you find them all?

Answers on page 136.

Puppies for Sale!

Which puppy will get picked? First, find all matching pairs, and the one puppy left is the one that gets picked!

81   Answer on page 136.

FIRE ON ALL CYLINDERS!
Recycling Pathway
• •

Which paths lead the recyclers to the right bins?

Answers on page 136.

Picture This

Draw each of the 18 boxes in the 3 by 6 grid below so they form a picture of a narwhal (a small Arctic whale). Use the letters and numbers as a guide.

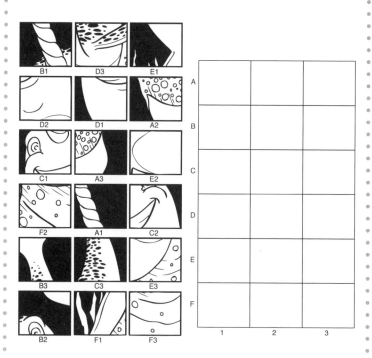

83   Answer on page 136.

M Is for Mountain

There are more than 15 things hidden in this picture that begin with the letter **M.** Can you find them all?

Answers on page 137.

Theme Park

This "ride" has a theme, but we can't tell you what it is. Place all the words in the boxes below—when you do, read the word created in the outlined boxes, from top to bottom, to reveal what the theme is.

BUNS

CHIPS

COLA

GRILL

HAMBURGERS

HOT DOGS

KETCHUP

MUSTARD

PAPER PLATES

PICKLES

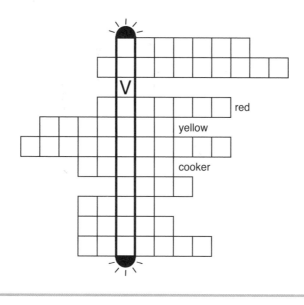

red

yellow

cooker

85   Answer on page 137.

Under the Sea

There are 10 differences bubbling between these 2 fishy illustrations. Can you find them all?

Answers on page 137.

Tangle

• •

Several paper clips have been laid on the table, one by
one. Which one is on the bottom of the pile?

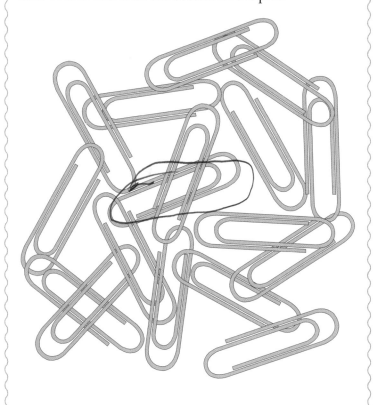

Face Off

Can you spot the 2 identical faces?

Answer on page 138.

Jurassic Scramble

Draw each of the 12 boxes in the 3 by 4 grid below so they form a picture of a prehistoric scene. We filled in the first one to get you started.

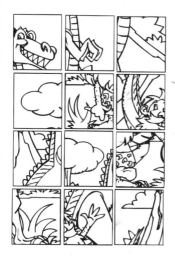
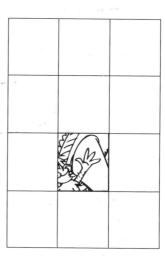

Answer on page 138.

Happy Birthday to Me!

How many different kinds of scrumptious cupcakes are there? Which kind appears the most? Find one that only appears once. Then unscramble all the letters to reveal the birthday boy's message.

Answers on page 138.

Family Ties

Divide the grid into 9 sections with each section containing 4 squares. Every section must contain one of each of the family members—mother, father, brother, and sister.

Hint: Look for places where the same family member is bunched together, and start there.

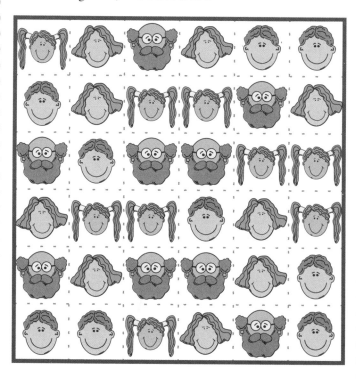

91   Answer on page 138.

Grandma's Cookies

The 10 objects listed are hidden in the picture below.
Can you find them all?

BASEBALL BAT ~~BASEBALL BAT~~

BUTTERFLY

BUTTON ~~BUTTON~~

CATERPILLAR

CRESCENT MOON

DISC ~~DISC~~

ENVELOPE ~~ENVELOPE~~

RING

SOCK

TACK

Answers on page 138.

Chain Words

• •

Place 2 letters in the middle squares that will complete one word and start another. For example, ER would complete FLY - ER - ROR.

Flower Growth

• •

Which of these flowers has the longest stem?

Answers on page 138.

Jack's Bewildering Beanstalk

Jack has to get up the beanstalk, but he needs your help to find the way!

94   Answer on page 139.

Rhyme Time

Each clue leads to a 2-word answer that rhymes, such as BIG PIG or STABLE TABLE. The numbers in parentheses after the clue give the number of letters in each word. For example, "cookware taken from the oven (3, 3)" would be "hot pot."

1. Appointment to wear wheeled shoes (5, 4): _____

2. Paperback thief (4, 5): _____

3. Fire in a confusing, winding pathway (4, 5):

   _____

4. Place for a container of soup (3, 4): _____

5. Opportunity to take a peek (6, 6): _____

6. Large town of felines (5, 4): _____

7. Good fortune on the hockey rink (4, 4): _____

8. Supporter of large vehicles (3, 3): _____

9. Famous mouse, covered in honey (6, 6): _____

10. Small building for storing toboggans (4, 4):

    _____

11. Warm up beef or pork (4, 4): _Heat, Meat_

12. Pursuit among the stars (5, 5): _____

Tangled Giraffes

These giraffes are in over their heads! Can you get through their maze of stripes?

Finish

Start

Answer on page 139.

Up in the Air

Which kite belongs to which child? Follow the strings.

Word Ladder

Can you change just one letter on each line to transform the top word to the bottom word? Don't change the order of the letters, and make sure you have a common English word at each step.

LESS

_____

_____

_____

MORE

Flippy Numbers

Below is an incorrect equation. Can you swap 2 of the number cards to get a correct equation?

$$30 - 14 = 36 - 28$$

Answers on page 139.

Unk the Caveman

Which caveman is the mirror image of the caveman in the box?

Answer on page 140.

Puppies Galore!

Every dog breed listed is contained within the group of letters on the next page. Breeds can be found in a straight line horizontally, vertically, or diagonally. They may be read either forward or backward.

AIREDALE	PEKINGESE
AKITA	POINTER
BASSET HOUND	POODLE
BEAGLE	PUG
BOXER	RETRIEVER
BULLDOG	ROTTWEILER
CHIHUAHUA	SAMOYED
CHOW	SCHNAUZER
COLLIE	SETTER
DALMATIAN	SHAR-PEI
DOBERMAN	SHEEPDOG
GREAT DANE	SPANIEL
GREYHOUND	SPITZ
HUSKY	TERRIER
LHASA APSO	WELSH CORGI
MASTIFF	WHIPPET

```
B L P A O N G R E Y H O U N D Z F
L S O W S E G R E T R I E V E R E
D C I E P R A H S T E G A O P K S
K H Z W A O C P P I T R S P J V E
F N L R A J O M E S H E E P D O G
J A G S S U W D X L P A S Q N F N
C U R S A R D A L M A T I A N X I
C Z T E H M E W J E E D R P U G K
H E E F L B O T A D I A E Z I C E
I R P B Y I E Y N Q L N I R T Y P
H M P B U K E A E I L E S P I T Z
U A I O V D S W G D O B E R M A N
A S H X A M C U T L C P W I W Y S
H T W E D N U O H T E S S A B L K
U I I R E I R R E T O N C H O W K
A F I K W E L S H C O R G I T A W
F F S P A N I E L D B U L L D O G
```

B Is for Bird-Watching

How many things can you find that start with the letter **B**? Finding 30 would be BEAUTIFUL. Finding more than 40 would be the BEST!

Answers on page 140.

Road Trip!

This confused driver is having trouble finding the gas station—and he's running on empty! Follow the arrows to help him find the correct route.

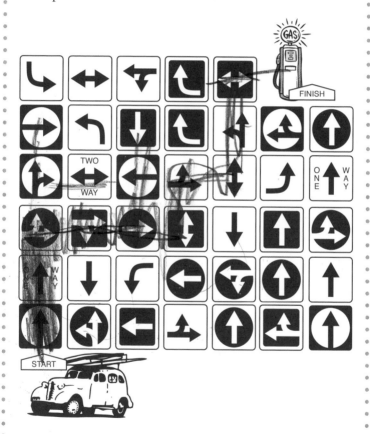

Answer on page 140.

Pic-doku

• •

The grid below is divided into 4 sections. Your job is to have each of the 4 items appear once in each section and in each row and column. Fill each square with the item's image or the letter that represents it. No item can repeat in any section, row, or column.

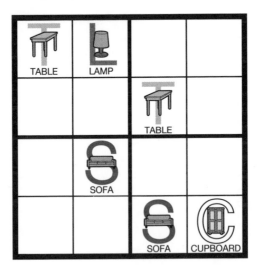

Answer on page 141.

Anagrammar

There are 2 words on this torn parchment that are anagrams (rearrangements of the same letters) of each other. Trace the lines to the connecting circle, and write in the identical letter to discover the second word.

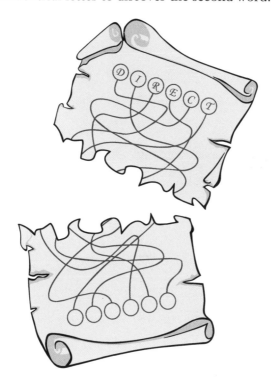

Answer on page 141.

Where's My Ball?

How many different kinds of balls do you see? Which kind appears the most? The ball that appears only once is my favorite, can you find it? Then unscramble the letters to spell my favorite game!

On Your Mark, Get Set, Go!

Find the path to the nuts! Then unscramble all the letters for a happy solution.

107   Answers on page 141.

Crosspic

Looks like someone put pictures in this puzzle where there are supposed to be words! See if you can fill in the grid by writing the word—one letter for each box—that names each of the pictures. Words run across and down.

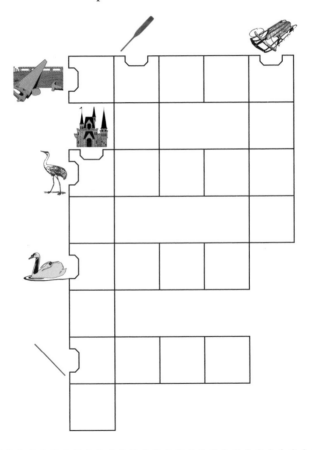

Answers on page 141.

Forest Friends

• •

Draw each of the 12 boxes in the 3 by 4 grid below so they form a picture of some forest creatures. We filled in one to get you started.

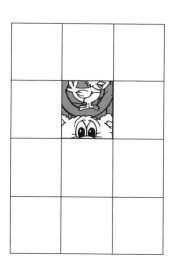

109   Answer on page 142.

Halloween Costumes

ACROSS

1. Papas' partners
6. Energy
9. Wipe away
10. Close tightly
11. Soldier costume: 2 wds.
12. Skin openings
14. Slip on
15. Costume for a girl named Montana
16. Boy's name (hidden in "solar energy")
18. Pig pen
19. Unusual
21. Perform in plays
24. Barnyard milk giver
27. Doll costume
30. Pops
32. Boy's name (rearrange "to lie")
33. Christmassy costume
35. Young fellows
36. Church instrument
37. Clever
38. Bedtime tale

DOWN

1. Girl's name (hidden in "home game")
2. Dry as a desert
3. Very important
4. All together: 2 wds.
5. "Told ya!"
6. Lowly worker
7. Makes, as money
8. Dress fold
10. Tub with a whirlpool
13. Not outgoing
15. Row of bushes
17. "I don't think so"
20. Hairstyle
21. President on a penny
22. Contacts by phone
23. Courtroom event
25. Not together
26. Ballroom dance
28. Your physical self
29. "_____ about time!"
31. Twinkling light in the sky
33. Distress signal
34. "...have you _____ wool?"

111   Answers on page 142.

D Is for Dock

There are more than 10 things hidden in this picture that begin with the letter **D.** How many can you find?

Answers on page 142.

Family Ties

Divide the grid into 9 sections with each section containing 4 squares. Every section must contain one of each of the family members—mother, father, brother, and sister.

Hint: Look for places where the same family member is bunched together, and start there.

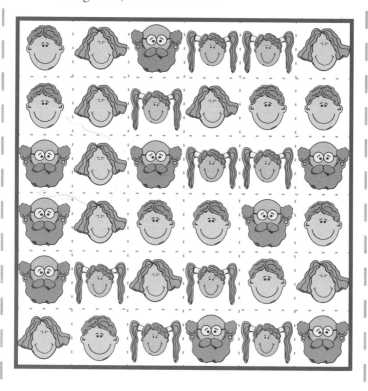

Answer on page 142.

Wacky Waterslide

Help Jimmy find the correct water chute that will lead him to the pool below.

Answer on page 143.

On Safari

Each explorer has one extra detail that the others do not. Can you spot each detail?

Answers on page 143.

Pic-doku

The grid below is divided into 4 sections. Your job is to have each of the 4 items appear once in each section and in each row and column. Fill each square with the item's image or the letter that represents it. No item can repeat in any section, row, or column.

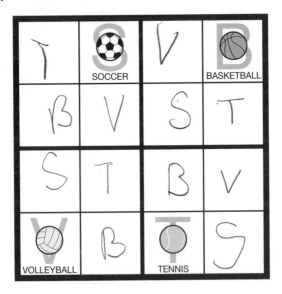

116

Answer on page 143.

Dozen Leaves Blots

Two of the blots below are identical in shape and color.
Can you find them?

117   Answer on page 143.

Something's Fishy

How many different kinds of fish are there? Which fish only appears once? Which fish appears the most? Unscramble all the letters for a message.

Answers on page 143.

Monster Party!

Each row of monsters (horizontal and vertical) has one thing in common. Find each, and you'll be a monstrous success!

Answers on page 144.

Beach Bum

Surf's up, dude! Before you hit the waves, can you find the words in the grid below for the 6 items indicated by the arrows in the picture? Words can be found in a straight line horizontally, vertically, or diagonally. They may be read either forward or backward.

```
D F L E W Q I S I C C A
S R K Q V A Q R U X M H
T M A V B S O O N N G H
L C B O T B E A C H L R
W I H R B Y F O D C L T
B N O C O F S C A T A H
Z H U U Y S R R F Y B H
S D Y G P Q C U B E E D
M H C O J S W M S J S O
N K F A M L T R Z T A M
S E S S A L G N U S B X
S F O B A D Q Q I M Z P
X I Y W Q Q Z H X K Y R
```

Face Off

. . . .

Can you spot the 2 identical faces?

Answer on page 144.

ANSWERS

Rhyme Time (page 6)

yum, drum, thumb, crumb, from

Chain Words (page 7)

Flower Growth (page 7)

Dot-to-Dot (page 8)

Rock On! (page 9)

C. In A, the guitar has a black strap; in B, the T-shirt has a design on it.

Alien Message (page 10)

"Take me to your weeder."

R Is for River (page 11)

rabbit, raccoon, raft, rainbow, rapids, rhinoceros, ring, rocks, roof, rooster, rope, rowboat

Flippy Numbers (page 12)

Word Ladder (page 12)

RING, sing, sins, sons, tons, TOSS

Pic-doku (page 13)

Big Cheese (pages 16-17)

One Small Step (page 14)

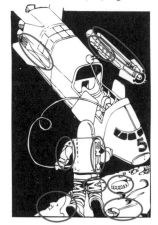

Tangle (page 18)

Picture-by-Number (page 15)

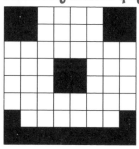

Answers

Fairy Find (page 19)

1. antenna; 2. cap; 3. flowers;
4. belt; 5. spotted wings;
6. pointed ears

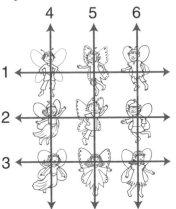

Black Diamonds (page 20)

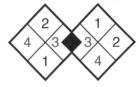

Chain Words (page 20)

Family Ties (page 21)

Dot-to-Dot (page 22)

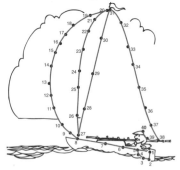

A Bug's Life (page 23)

Dino Crusade (page 24)

Rhyme Time (page 25)

Anagrammar (page 26)
THING

Ice Capades (page 27)

Picture Day (page 28)

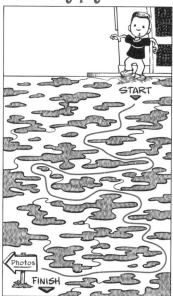

Word Ladder (page 29)
Answers may vary.
DOG, dot, pot, PET

Flower Growth (page 29)

125

Answers

A Bright Idea (page 30)
A. B is missing the filament;
C is missing the threads.

Mutation (page 31)
COLLIEFORNIA

Nine Fish Blots (page 32)

Rhyme Time (page 33)
1. likes bikes; 2. rare bear;
3. bake cake; 4. wild child;
5. bright light

Chain Words (page 33)

School Daze (page 34)

Jumbled Up (page 35)

So You Want to Be a Star!
(page 35)

The Solar System
(pages 36–37)

```
A R F       A W E
L O I S     M A R S
P L U T O   S P L I T
R O T ■ B A H ■ K E Y
O W E N ■ C U S S
      E A R T H
    I D L E ■ H E R S
R A G ■ A S A ■ R O O
A T L A S ■ V E N U S
M O O N ■ A S I S
  P O T       S E E
```

Zoom (page 38)

G 4   C 3   E 4   D 1   A 6

Up in the Air (page 39)

Ahoy, Matey! (page 40)

pail, palm tree, parrot, parachute, patch, pear, pearls, pelican, penguin, pineapple, pirate, plank, plant, ponytail, pot, puddle

Nine Pawprints Blots
(page 41)

127

Answers

At the Petting Zoo (pages 42–43)

Leftover letters spell: What has six eyes but cannot see? Three blind mice!

```
W H A D S T H A S S S
I X E K O S G N Y G E
S T C S H N E O U B U
S U O E A K K I A S T
D Y E R C M N E E T R
S P E I T E A I Y A S
C L H K A O N L B S A
N C E P R O I B L N O
T S I M P U I S E E T
H G R E A T T E E B L
S I N D S C M I C S E
```

Tangle (page 46)

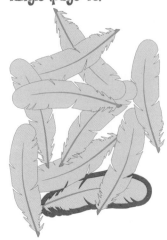

Family Ties (page 44)

Dot-to-Dot (page 47)

Big Top Maze (page 45)

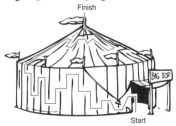

Flippy Numbers (page 48)

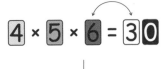

Jumbled Up (page 48)

Rhyme Time (page 49)

Haunted Scramble (page 50)

G H O S T
HGOTS

C O B W E B S
WOCBESB

S P I D E R
PDEISR

B L A C K C A T
BLCKA TCA

S K U L L
KLSUL

Flower Growth (page 51)

Answers

Swamp Things (page 52)

Family Ties (page 53)

Big Builder (page 54)

Nine Stars Blots (page 55)

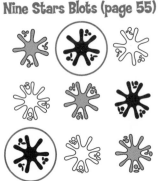

130

dd It Up! (page 56)

HY DID THE MATH BOOK NEED GLASSES?

HE HAD PROBLEMS WITH

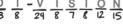

$$\frac{D}{3} \frac{I}{8} - \frac{V}{24} \frac{I}{8} \frac{S}{7} \frac{I}{8} \frac{O}{12} \frac{N}{15}$$

$V = 12 + 12$ $D = 11 + 2$

$O = 5 + 7$ $N = 8 + 7$

$I = 6 + 2$ $S = 3 + 4$

rosspic (page 57)

Find the Differences (pages 58-59)

Road Trip! (page 60)

Take a Note (page 61)

D. A's pencil has 2 bands; B's pad is missing rings; C is holding a brush; E has black pants.

Answers

Good Luck! (pages 62-63)

B	A	D		P	A	D		D	I	M
A	G	E		A	C	E		O	D	E
R	A	B	B	I	T	S	F	O	O	T
	I	R	O	N		E	A	R	L	
	N	A	Y		A	R	T	S		
			E	A	T					
	Y	E	A	H		P	A	S		
	H	U	B	S		A	I	N	T	
N	U	M	B	E	R	S	E	V	E	N
E	L	M		L	O	P		I	V	E
W	A	Y		S	O	S		L	E	T

Hairdresser! (page 64)

Pic-doku (page 65)

After School (page 66)

Tangle (page 67)

132

Poolside Penguins (page 68)

Flower Growth (page 69)

Mouse Hunt! (page 70)

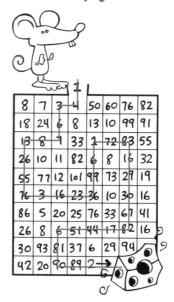

Nippy Numbers (page 69)

$295 \div 5 = 59$

$295 \div 5 = 19$

Answers

Distant Visitor (page 71)

L Is for Lunchtime (page 74)

ladder, lamb, laptop, lawn mower, leaves, legs, lemons, lens, lion, lizard, lumberjack, lunch box

Go Fish (page 75)

Searching for Shrek! (pages 72-73)

On Top of Spaghetti (page 76)

Recess Scramble (page 78)

PLAYGROUND
ORGUDYNALP

JUMP ROPE
PPROEMJU

TEETER-TOTTER
EETTOEETRTTR

SLIDE
LDISE

SWINGS
GSINWS

BASKETBALL
TEKBLALBAS

Family Ties (page 77)

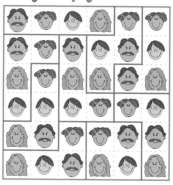

Nine Leaves Blots (page 79)

135

Answers

Ski Fun (page 80)

1. Banana as snowman's nose;
2. cowboy hat on skier; 3. lost
surfer; 4. man buried in snow;
5. taxi cab on slope; 6. sheep in
chair lift; 7. elephant skiing;
8. man skiing up the hill;
9. helicopter flying upside
down; 10. hot air balloon
flying sideways

Puppies for Sale! (page 81)

Recycling Pathway (page 82)

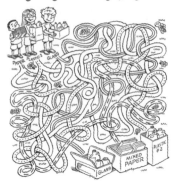

Picture This (page 83)

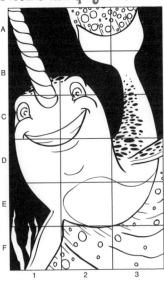

M Is for Mountain (page 84)

mask, math problem, medal, mitt, mixer, Mona Lisa, money, monkey, moon, moose, mop, mountain, mouse, mouth, muffin, mushroom

Under the Sea (page 86)

Theme Park (page 85)

Tangle (page 87)

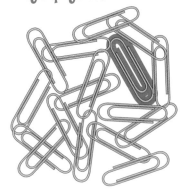

137

Answers

Face Off (page 88)

Family Ties (page 91)

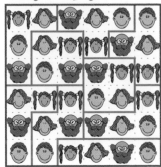

Jurassic Scramble (page 89)

Grandma's Cookies (page 92)

Happy Birthday to Me! (page 90)

There are 5 different kinds of cupcakes.

 I'M GOING TO BE TEN

This cupcake ( ) appears the most.

This cupcake ( ) appears only once.

Chain Words (page 93)

 WRISTAMP

Flower Growth (page 93)

Jack's Bewildering Beanstalk (page 94)

Rhyme Time (page 95)

1. skate date; 2. book crook;
3. maze blaze; 4. pot spot;
5. glance chance; 6. kitty city;
7. puck luck; 8. van fan;
9. sticky Mickey; 10. sled shed;
11. heat meat; 12. space chase

Tangled Giraffes (page 96)

Up in the Air (page 97)

Word Ladder (page 98)

Answers may vary.
LESS, loss, lose, lore, MORE

Flippy Numbers (page 98)

30 - 14 = 36 - 28

30 - 18 = 36 - 24

Answers

Unk the Caveman (page 99)

Puppies Galore! (pages 100-101)

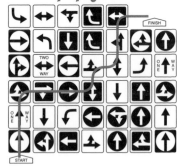

B Is for Bird-Watching (page 102)

baby, back, backpack, badminton birdie, badminton racket, bag, bald eagle, bald man, ball, baseball bat, baseball cap, bats, beanie, bed, beehive, bees, bell, belt, berries, bib, bicycle, biker, binoculars, birds, bird-watcher, blackbird, blanket, blindfold, blocks, bodies, bone, bouquet, bow, bow tie, box, boy, bride, buckle, bull, bulldog, bump, bun, bunny, burger, bushes, butterfly

Road Trip! (page 103)

Pic-doku (page 104)

TABLE	LAMP	CUPBOARD	SOFA
SOFA	CUPBOARD	TABLE	LAMP
CUPBOARD	SOFA	LAMP	TABLE
LAMP	TABLE	SOFA	CUPBOARD

Anagrammar (page 105)

CREDIT

Where's My Ball? (page 106)

There are 5 different kinds of balls.

C H A S E   T H E   B A L L !

This ball ( ) appears the most.

This ball ( ) appears only once.

On Your Mark, Get Set, Go! (page 107)

Crosspic (page 108)

141

Answers

Forest Friends (page 109)

Halloween Costumes (pages 110–111)

D Is for Dock (page 112)

deer, derby (hat), dinghy, dinosaur, diver, dock, dog, doll, dolphin, donkey, doughnuts, dress, drum, duck

Family Ties (page 113)

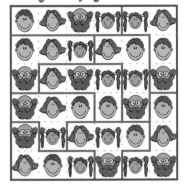

Wacky Waterslide (page 114)

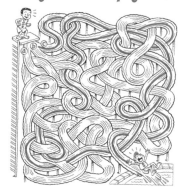

On Safari (page 115)

Pic-doku (page 116)

Dozen Leaves Blots (page 117)

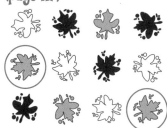

Something's Fishy (page 118)

There are 5 different kinds of fish.

I LOVE TO WATCH FISH

This fish ( ) appears once.

This fish () appears the most.

143

Answers

Monster Party! (page 119)

1. horns; 2. clawed feet;
3. sharp teeth; 4. fur; 5. tails;
6. angry eyes

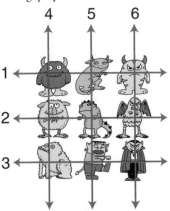

Face Off (page 121)

Beach Bum (page 120)